NO AR

SO-AKK-997

DISCARD

Erickson School
1040 Pearl Avenue
San Jose, Calif. 95126

Frederick Douglass

Frederick Douglass, born into slavery in 1818, educated himself, escaped from captivity, and went on to become one of America's greatest antislavery crusaders.

JUNIOR ■ WORLD ■ BIOGRAPHIES

Frederick Douglass

MELISSA BANTA

CHELSEA JUNIORS

a division of CHELSEA HOUSE PUBLISHERS

Chelsea House Publishers

EDITORIAL DIRECTOR   Richard Rennert
EXECUTIVE MANAGING EDITOR   Karyn Gullen Browne
EXECUTIVE EDITOR   Sean Dolan
COPY CHIEF   Philip Koslow
ART DIRECTOR   Nora Wertz
PICTURE EDITOR   Adrian G. Allen
MANUFACTURING DIRECTOR   Gerald Levine
SYSTEMS MANAGER   Lindsey Ottman
PRODUCTION COORDINATOR   Marie Claire Cebrián-Ume

JUNIOR WORLD BIOGRAPHIES

SENIOR EDITOR   Kathy Kuhtz

Staff for FREDERICK DOUGLASS

ASSOCIATE EDITOR   Terrance Dolan
EDITORIAL ASSISTANT   Robert Kimball Green
SENIOR DESIGNER   Marjorie Zaum
PICTURE RESEARCHER   Nisa Rauschenberg
COVER ILLUSTRATION   Alan J. Nahigian

Copyright © 1993 by Chelsea House Publishers, a division of Main Line
Book Co. All rights reserved. Printed and bound in the United States of
America.

First printing

1 3 5 7 9 8 6 4 2

Library of Congress Cataloging-in-Publication Data
Banta, Melissa.
  Frederick Douglass / Melissa Banta
    p. cm.—(Junior world biographies)
  Includes biographical references and index.
Summary: A biography of the man who, after escaping slavery, became an
orator, writer, and leader in the anti-slavery movement in the nineteenth
century.
ISBN 0-7910-1765-6
ISBN 0-7910-1973-X (pbk.)
1. Douglass, Frederick, 1817–1895—Juvenile literature. 2. Abolitionists—
United States—Biography—Juvenile literature. 3. Afro-Americans—Biog-
raphy—Juvenile literature. 4. Slavery—United States—Anti-slavery
movements—Juvenile literature. [1. Douglass, Frederick, 1817–1895. 2.
Abolitionists. 3. Afro-Americans—Biography.]
I. Title. II. Series.
E449.D75B36 1993   92-18292
973.8'092—dc20   CIP
[B]   AC

Contents

On many southern plantations, black women raised their children while the men worked the fields. As a child, Douglass was taken care of by his grandmother, Betsey Bailey.

1

"Why Am I a Slave?"

Frederick Douglass did not know that he was a slave until he was six years old. His original name was Frederick Bailey. He was born in February 1818 in a wooden cabin near Easton, Maryland, not far from Chesapeake Bay. He did not know who his father was, although he heard rumors that he was a white man. Frederick's mother worked long hours as a slave on a plantation, and Frederick did not see her much. His grandmother, Betsey Bailey, took care of Frederick and his brothers, sisters, and cousins. Frederick spent many happy days playing in the woods, unaware that he was owned by a wealthy white family.

When Frederick turned six, his grandmother told him that they were going to take a long journey. After walking many miles, they came to a big house. Frederick had never seen such a house. His grandmother told him to play with the other children who were there. Some of them were Frederick's relatives. The young boy was afraid. He felt that something bad was going to happen. Suddenly, one of the children told Frederick that his grandmother had gone. Frederick ran out to the road, but his grandmother had disappeared. He flung himself on the ground and cried. At that moment his happy childhood ended. His life as a slave had begun.

Unlike white Americans, black men and women had not come to America because they wanted to. Instead, they had been brought to the United States against their will. Captured and taken by force from their homes in Africa by white slave traders, they were brought to America in chains aboard slave ships. Most of them were then sold to plantation owners in the southern United States, where slavery was legal. The southern *economy* depended on agriculture—especially the growing of cotton and tobacco—and slaves provided cheap labor for the plantation owners who grew these products.

Slaves led a miserable existence. They had no more rights than animals. Some slaves were given sufficient food and clothing and treated decently, but more often they were starved, beaten, and forced to live under terrible conditions. Most of them spent their days laboring from sunrise to sunset in the cotton fields. At the whim of a plantation owner, slaves found themselves lined up like livestock to be sold to another plantation. When this happened, slaves were often separated from their friends and families forever.

The big house where Frederick had been left by his grandmother belonged to Captain Aaron Anthony, who managed a large plantation where

Southern plantation owners examine slaves to be purchased. Young black children were often bought and taken away from their families to work on different plantations.

more than 300 slaves labored. Working for Captain Anthony, young Frederick was quickly introduced to the sorrow and misery of slavery. "I suffered much from hunger, but much more from cold," Frederick wrote years later. "In the coldest winter I was kept almost naked." Frederick had no clothes except "a coarse torn linen shirt, touching only to my knees. . . . On the coldest nights, I used to steal a bag which was used for carrying corn to the mill. I would crawl into this bag, and there sleep on the cold, damp, clay floor, with my head in and feet out." Like cattle, Frederick and other slave children ate cornmeal from a trough. They had only oyster shells or crude, makeshift spoons with which to scoop out the food.

One night, Frederick saw Captain Anthony whipping his Aunt Hester. It was the first of many beatings that he would witness or experience himself. "The louder she screamed, the harder he whipped," Frederick remembered. After witnessing another such beating, Frederick asked himself, "Why am I a slave?" He cried and wondered "how [God] could do this and be good."

One of Frederick's jobs was to run errands for Lucretia Auld, Captain Anthony's daughter. Lucretia liked Frederick. When Frederick turned eight, Lucretia told him that he would be sent to the home of Hugh Auld, Lucretia's brother-in-law.

Hugh Auld and his wife, Sophia, lived in Baltimore, Maryland, where Hugh managed a ship-building company.

In Baltimore, Frederick did small jobs and took care of the Aulds' infant son, Tommy. Like Lucretia, Sophia Auld became a friend to Frederick. He described Sophia as "a woman of the kindest heart and the finest feeling." She encouraged him to abandon his timid manner and look people in the eye. And she began teaching Frederick how to read, even though it was illegal in the South for slaves to learn to read and write. When Sophia told her husband that she was educating the young slave, Hugh Auld became enraged. What she was doing was against the law, Auld told her. He warned that slaves who could read might learn to think for themselves and become dangerous. After this, Frederick noticed a change in Sophia. She now treated him as a piece of property instead of a friend and a human being. "Her tender heart became stone," Frederick sadly observed.

Because of Auld's reaction to his wife's attempt to educate Frederick, Frederick realized how important education must be. He continued his schooling on his own, determined to learn to read and write. He collected newspapers and books in secret and slipped away to study them whenever he could, even though he risked severe punishment.

As his reading skills improved, Frederick read everything that he could about the institution of slavery. He read about the *free states* in the North, where there was no slavery. He read about slave rebellions and about *abolitionists*, people who were working to end slavery in the United States. "The more I read, the more I was led to [hate] my enslavers," he later recalled. Men like Captain Anthony and Hugh Auld, he decided, were "a band of . . . robbers, who had . . . gone to Africa, and stolen us from our homes, and in a strange land reduced us to slavery."

One of Frederick's most prized books was called *The Columbian Orator*. It was a collection of essays and speeches about freedom and *democracy*. An essay about the injustice of slavery especially inspired the young slave. Frederick dreamed of writing such an essay himself one day.

In 1833, Lucretia Auld died, and Frederick, now 15, became the property of her husband, Thomas Auld. (Frederick had become Lucretia Auld's property when her father, Aaron Anthony, died.) Auld wanted Frederick to work on his farm in the town of St. Michaels, Maryland. Uprooted from the friends that he had made in Baltimore, Frederick was sent to labor in the fields on Auld's farm. Frederick came to hate slavery even more under Thomas Auld, who was a cruel master. He gave his slaves little food and whipped them regularly.

Thomas Auld found Frederick to be too independent minded, and so he sent the boy to Edward Covey. Covey had earned a reputation as a "slave breaker," who could make even the most defiant slaves meek and obedient. In addition to working long, hard hours in heat, rain, or snow, barely a week went by when Frederick did not receive a brutal beating. "Mr. Covey succeeded in breaking me," Frederick remembered. "I was broken in body, soul, and spirit."

But Frederick did not remain "broken" for long. One day, Frederick decided that it was time to fight back. When Covey attempted to beat him, Frederick resisted. The slave and his master fought. The battle lasted for nearly two hours, and when it was over, the slave was the victor. Frederick risked severe punishment, and even death, for violently rising up against his master. But Covey was too embarrassed to tell others that his own slave had beaten him, and Frederick went unpunished. Covey never whipped him again. "I was a changed being after that fight," Frederick wrote about the incident. "It recalled to life my crushed self-respect and my self-confidence, and inspired me with a renewed determination to be a FREEMAN."

In 1835, at age 18, Douglass and five other slaves planned to escape to freedom in the North. Their plot was uncovered, however, and Frederick was sent to work in the city of Baltimore, Maryland.

2

Quest for
Freedom

In 1835, Edward Covey sent Frederick to work on
a nearby farm owned by a man named William
Freeland. With his newly won self-respect and
self-confidence, the young slave began his career
as an educator and leader. He started a secret
school for blacks, even though he was only a
teenager himself. The school met at night in
an out-of-the-way place, where Frederick would
teach his students how to read, write, and think
like free human beings. In the meantime, Frederick

and five other slaves began plotting an escape to the North. They planned to steal a boat, row to the north end of Chesapeake Bay, and from there to head for the free state of Pennsylvania. But just before they were about to make their getaway, their plot was discovered, and they were arrested and thrown in jail.

Thomas Auld retrieved Frederick from jail and sent him back to Hugh Auld in Baltimore. This turned out to be a lucky break for Frederick, who could have been punished harshly. Frederick was now 18 years old and six feet tall, a strong, sure-handed young man. Hugh Auld decided to hire out Frederick as a ship caulker, a worker who seals the seams of boats to prevent water from seeping through.

Although he was severely beaten one day by a gang of white workers, life on the Baltimore docks was better than life as a plantation field hand. Frederick received wages like any other dockworker. Although he turned most of the money over to Hugh Auld each week, he was allowed to keep some. And in Baltimore, Frederick had a chance to associate with other educated blacks, many of whom were free. He discussed books, politics, and ideas about freedom and democracy with his new friends. He also met Anna Murray, a free black woman who worked as a servant for a local family. Soon Frederick and Anna became engaged.

Although Frederick's life was more comfortable, he was still a slave, the property of a white man. "Whenever my condition was improved," he wrote, "it only increased my desire to be free." One day, Frederick was late in turning over his wages to Auld. Furious, Auld took away Frederick's privileges. Frederick had had enough. He made up his mind to do what he had been dreaming of for years. He would attempt an escape to the North—to freedom.

Frederick planned his escape carefully. For a runaway slave, capture could mean death or a lifetime of backbreaking labor in the hot cotton fields of the Deep South. Frederick could be sure that if this attempt failed, he would not get another chance. He would travel in disguise, as a sailor. From a friend, he obtained a navy uniform and documents that identified him as a sailor and a free man. He hoped that this false identity would protect him from the slave hunters who were always on the lookout for runaways.

A poster offers a $100 reward for an escaped slave in Missouri. A description of the runaway slave is included to help slave catchers. In 1838, Douglass joined the ranks of fugitive slaves when he fled from Baltimore to New York City.

$100 REWARD!

RANAWAY

From the undersigned, living on Current River, about twelve miles above Doniphan,

in Ripley County, Mo., on 2nd of March, 1860, **A NE GRO MAN**, about 30 years old, weighs about 160 pounds; high forehead, with a scar on it; had on brown pants and coat very much worn, and an old black wool hat; shoes size No. 11.

The above reward will be given to any person who may apprehend this said negro out of the State; and fifty dollars if apprehended in this State outside of Ripley county, or $25 if taken in Ripley county.

APOS TUCKER.

On September 3, 1838, Frederick boarded a train bound for Wilmington, Delaware. As the train rolled through Delaware, a *slave state*, Frederick nervously watched the other passengers. He sat in an agony of suspense every time the train stopped, expecting to be arrested at any moment. He felt, he recalled, like "a murderer fleeing justice." At Wilmington, he boarded a steamboat for Philadelphia. Once the boat passed into Pennsylvania, a free state, he breathed a little easier. Now he thought sadly about the friends whom he had left behind in Baltimore, and especially Anna.

From Philadelphia, Frederick took a train to New York City. He arrived on September 4 and quickly lost himself in the great throngs of people on the streets of the crowded city. In his heart was a tremendous joy. "A new world had opened upon me," he realized.

A poster warns escaped slaves from the South living in Boston to beware of slave catchers hunting runaways in the North. Douglass moved to New Bedford, Massachusetts, from New York after he had escaped from Maryland, and he lived in constant fear of slave catchers.

CAUTION!!

COLORED PEOPLE

OF BOSTON, ONE & ALL,

You are hereby respectfully CAUTIONED and advised, to avoid conversing with the

Watchmen and Police Officers of Boston,

For since the recent ORDER OF THE MAYOR & ALDERMEN, they are empowered to act as

KIDNAPPERS

AND

Slave Catchers,

And they have already been actually employed in KIDNAPPING, CATCHING, AND KEEPING SLAVES. Therefore, if you value your LIBERTY, and the *Welfare of the Fugitives* among you, *Shun* them in every possible manner, as so many *HOUNDS* on the track of the most unfortunate of your race.

Keep a Sharp Look Out for KIDNAPPERS, and have TOP EYE open.

APRIL 24, 1851.

3

Challenges
of Freedom

Although he had reached the North, Frederick soon learned that he was not completely safe. Other blacks whom he talked to in the city told him that slave catchers roamed the streets, hunting for runaways. After several fearful days and nights spent wandering around the city, Frederick was befriended by a black sailor, who introduced him to David Ruggles.

Ruggles was a part of the *Underground Railroad*, a network of people who helped runaway slaves escape safely from the South to the North. Slaves traveled along the "railroad" at night, hidden in barrels or under piles of hay on wagons. At the Underground Railroad "stations," abolitionists would hide the fugitives in their attics, cellars, or barns. Moving from hiding place to hiding place, runaway slaves would eventually reach safety in the North.

A stop on the Underground Railroad, a network of hiding places where escaped slaves found shelter from their pursuers during their flight to freedom in the North.

Ruggles invited Frederick to stay in his home, where he would be safe from slave catchers. Soon after, Frederick sent for Anna Murray, who quickly joined him in New York. They were married a short time later. Ruggles suggested that Frederick and Anna go to New Bedford, Massachusetts. There were many blacks and abolitionists in Massachusetts, making it one of

the safest free states for former slaves. And New Bedford was a whaling town, where Frederick might be able to find a job as a ship caulker.

Frederick and Anna made their way to New Bedford. There, they found lodgings with a prosperous black family. Still worried about slave catchers, Frederick decided to change his name. He began calling himself Frederick Douglass, instead of Frederick Bailey. Within a few short years, the name Frederick Douglass would be known throughout America and even in Europe. But first, Douglass was faced with the challenge of making his way as a free man.

In New Bedford, Douglass did not have to live in hiding as he had in New York. For the first time, he saw what life was like in a free state. In Massachusetts, blacks lived without fear of the slave driver's whip. They worked for their own wages. Many of them were very successful and lived in their own houses. Black children went to the same schools as white children. It was much different from the way things were in the South.

Even though there was no slavery in Massachusetts, there was still the ugliness of *racism*. *Segregation* was enforced in some places, such as churches where blacks were made to sit in separate sections from whites. White people usually got the best jobs, and many blacks lived in poverty. And most white workers did not like to work with blacks. This made it hard for black workers like Douglass to find good jobs. Unable to land a job as a caulker, Douglass took whatever work he could find. He shoveled coal, loaded and unloaded ships, and operated a bellows in a brass foundry. Anna, in the meantime, found work as a maid.

It was only a matter of time before Douglass became involved in the thriving antislavery movement in Massachusetts. In New Bedford, he read his first issue of *The Liberator*, an abolitionist newspaper published by William Lloyd Garrison. Garrison was one of the best-known abolitionists in the United States. He was the leader of the American Anti-Slavery Society. He had dedicated his life to the fight against slavery. He also campaigned for equal rights for women.

Douglass read every issue of *The Liberator* that he could get his hands on. "The paper became my meat and drink," he remembered. "My soul was set on fire." Inspired by the words that he read in *The Liberator*, Douglass himself became an active antislavery spokesman in New Bedford. He joined the Zion Methodist Church for blacks. At church services, he made speeches against slavery. He began to acquire a reputation as a powerful public speaker.

In August 1841, Douglass was invited to give a speech at a meeting of the Massachusetts branch of the American Anti-Slavery Society. William Lloyd Garrison was in the audience. Garrison was impressed by Douglass's commanding presence, rich speaking voice, and captivating words. He was introduced to the young former slave after the meeting. Garrison immediately asked Douglass to be a speaker for the society. Douglass accepted. He began touring the northern states, giving speeches against slavery. Frederick Douglass had found his life's work.

Douglass was a stirring public speaker. He communicated the misery of slavery to his audiences by describing what it was like to be a slave. His reputation spread. Large crowds turned out to hear him speak. But life as an antislavery crusader was not easy. It was often dangerous, for not everybody in the North opposed slavery and racism. Douglass often faced angry, proslavery crowds when he gave a speech. But he would not

William Lloyd Garrison, one of the most influential abolitionists of his day and publisher of the antislavery newspaper The Liberator. *Douglass was greatly influenced by what he read in* The Liberator.

back down to racists. On segregated trains and steamships, he would refuse to sit in the sections set aside for blacks. "Refusing to obey, I was often dragged out of my seat, beaten, and severely bruised," he wrote.

As Douglass continued to lecture, his skills as a public speaker improved steadily. Soon, he could give as fine a speech as any politician or actor. In fact, he became so good at giving speeches that many people found it hard to believe that he was actually a former slave. It would be hard for Douglass to get his message across if people thought that he was a fake. He needed to convince them that he was telling the truth about his past, or his speeches would mean nothing.

Douglass came to a decision. He would write a book about his life. It would be a detailed account of his days as a slave in Maryland. His book would include all the facts about his past, including his real name. Douglass was taking a big risk in writing such a book. It would be an open invitation for slave catchers to hunt him down and return him to his former owner in Maryland. But Douglass was determined to tell the true story of his life.

Narrative of the Life of Frederick Douglass, an American Slave, was published in May 1845. The book was an instant best-seller. All over the United States, people read about the slave who had educated himself and escaped to freedom in the North. And through Douglass's writing, Americans everywhere experienced the horrors of slavery. After the publication of his *Narrative*, nobody could doubt that Frederick Douglass was telling the truth about himself and about the misery of slaves everywhere.

Douglass paid a price for publishing his autobiography. He had become an easy target for slave catchers. Fearing that the Aulds would send men to hunt him down and return him to slavery in Maryland, Douglass decided to leave the country. Douglass and Anna now had four children: Rosetta, Lewis, Frederick, and Charles. Douglass did not want to leave his family behind, but his freedom was at stake. In the summer of 1845, he sailed for England.

There was no slavery in England, and Douglass found that blacks were treated more fairly by the English. Douglass began giving speeches throughout England, Ireland, and Scotland. People there were sympathetic to his cause, and Douglass made many influential friends and gained a lot of support for the antislavery move-

The engraved portrait and title page of the first edition of Douglass's account of his life as a slave, published in 1845. The book, Narrative of the Life of Frederick Douglass, an American Slave, *brought home the grim realities of slavery to Americans throughout the country.*

ment in the United States. Douglass also spoke about other issues, such as alcohol. Douglass believed that liquor made blacks passive and weak, and he urged them not to drink it.

Despite the welcome that he had received in England, after two years there, Douglass was more than ready to return home. He missed his family, and he was eager to continue the fight against slavery in his own country. But he feared that slave catchers would grab him as soon as he set foot on American soil. Two of his English friends came to his rescue. They raised enough money to buy Douglass's freedom from the Auld family. The price of liberty was $710.96. Once the money was paid, Douglass was no longer the property of the Aulds, and he could return home without fear of slave catchers.

Douglass arrived back in America in 1847 as a man with an international reputation as a *civil rights* leader. During his absence, he had grown ever more popular with blacks and abolitionists in America. His book had helped to make him a living symbol of the fight against slavery. Douglass decided that it was time to start his own abolitionist newspaper. He moved his family from Massachusetts to Rochester, New York. There, he began to publish a weekly newspaper called the *North Star*. (In 1851, Douglass changed the name of his publication to *Frederick Douglass's Paper*.)

The *North Star* was an abolitionist newspaper, but it reported on women's rights issues as well. Like William Lloyd Garrison, Douglass saw that the struggles of women in America were similar to the struggles of blacks. Women were fighting for equal rights in American society, such as the right to vote. In the *North Star*, Douglass supported the *feminist* movement. And the feminists supported Douglass and the antislavery movement. Douglass became close friends with feminist leaders such as Susan B. Anthony and Lucretia Mott.

In addition to publishing the *North Star*, Douglass continued to make public speaking appearances. In Rochester, he fought for the desegregation of public schools. In 1857, Rochester's schools were finally desegregated, and white and black children sat in the same classrooms for the first time in that city. During this period, Douglass also took charge of the Underground Railroad in Rochester. Many runaway slaves found shelter in the home of the former slave from Maryland.

Douglass spent more and more time with other political leaders and important abolitionists. And he developed new ideas and opinions about the antislavery movement. William Lloyd Garrison disagreed with some of these opinions. Garrison, for example, felt that it would be wrong to use violence in the struggle against slavery. But Douglass had come to believe that peaceful means would not be enough to end slavery. Many other Americans believed—and feared—that this was true. In the coming years, their fears would grow as the slavery conflict in America became more and more violent. Eventually, the entire country would be engulfed in the violence.

A poster in Ashby, Massachusetts, announcing a discussion on the Fugitive Slave Bill in 1851. Abolitionists in the North were against the bill, which aided slave catchers from the South in their hunt for escaped slaves who had taken refuge in the North.

FUGITIVE
SLAVE BILL!

HON. HENRY WILSON

Will address the citizens on

Thursday Evening, April 3,

At the

At 7 o'clock, on the all-engrossing topics of the day—the FUGITIVE SLAVE BILL, the pro-slavery action of the National Government and the general aspect of the Slavery question.

Let every man and woman, without distinction of sect or party, attend the meeting and bear a testimony against the system which fills the prisons of a free republic with men whose only crime is a love of freedom—which strikes down the habeas corpus and trial by jury, and converts the free soil of Massachusetts into hunting ground for the Southern kidnappers.

Ashby, March 29, 1851.

White & Potter's Steam Press—4000 Impressions per hour—Spring Lane, Boston.

4

"Men of Color, to Arms"

Despite the efforts of abolitionists, the federal courts continued to uphold slavery in the South. The Fugitive Slave Act of 1850 struck a damaging blow against the antislavery movement. This *legislation* gave new legal rights to slave owners who pursued escaped slaves into free states. Slavery supporters won another important legal victory in 1857 with the historic Dred Scott decision.

Dred Scott was a slave owned by a man named John Emerson. When Emerson brought

Scott from the slave state of Missouri into the free state of Illinois, Scott went to court to try to obtain his freedom. Because he had been brought into a free state, Scott believed that he should be a free man. In 1857, the case reached the Supreme Court. In the North and the South, people waited anxiously for the court's decision. If the court ruled in favor of Dred Scott, it would be a great victory for slaves and abolitionists.

When the Supreme Court announced its decision, however, abolitionists were disappointed and enraged. The court stated that slaves had no rights as American citizens, even if they escaped to and lived in free northern states. Blacks in general, according to the Supreme Court, "had no rights which the white man was bound to respect." The Dred Scott decision told American blacks that they were no closer to achieving freedom and equality than they had ever been. Many abolitionists began to believe that it was time to take matters into their own hands. One of these men was John Brown.

John Brown was born in Connecticut in 1800. From his father, he inherited an intense hatred of slavery. During the 1820s and 1830s, the Brown home was a busy station on the Underground Railroad. During the 1850s, Brown became a well-known antislavery crusader. He did not shy away from the use of force in the struggle against slavery, and he had more than one violent encounter with proslavery activists. During these years, Douglass and Brown became friends and allies.

In October 1859, Brown led a group of antislavery fighters on a raid against a government weapons storehouse in Harpers Ferry, Virginia. Brown and his men planned to use the weapons to free slaves from local plantations. But government troops soon captured the raiders. Brown was hanged for the crime of treason.

Before he launched his raid on Harpers Ferry, Brown had written to Douglass and asked him to join in the action. Douglass decided not to participate because he believed that Brown's plot was a bad idea. But during the investigation of the incident, letters between Brown and Douglass, in which they discussed Brown's plans, were discovered. Douglass was accused of supporting the raid and participating in the plot. To avoid arrest, he fled to Canada. Once again, Frederick Douglass became a fugitive.

In Canada, Douglass continued his antislavery campaign, and soon he traveled to England again. Back in America, tensions between the North and the South over the issue of slavery were finally about to explode. The presidential election of 1860 became the focus of the conflict. If a president who did not fully support slavery was elected, the southern states threatened to break away from the United States and form their own nation. This act, known as *secession*, might lead to civil war.

In May 1860, Douglass received word that his youngest daughter, Annie, had died. By now, charges against Douglass related to the John

John Brown, the abolitionist freedom fighter, kisses a black infant before he is led away to be hanged for the crimes of treason and murder in 1859. Brown and his followers had attempted to start a slave uprising in Virginia that year.

Brown incident had been dropped. Grieving for the loss of his child, Douglass returned to America just as the coming storm finally broke.

The 1860 presidential election was won by Republican candidate Abraham Lincoln of Illinois. The South viewed Lincoln as hostile to their slavery-based economy and way of life. Unable to accept Lincoln as their president, the southern states began to secede from the Union. One by one, they declared that they were no longer part of the United States of America. By February 1861, South Carolina, Mississippi, Alabama, Georgia, Florida, Louisiana, and Texas had seceded. They would soon be followed by Virginia, North Carolina, Tennessee, and Arkansas. These states then banded together to form their own nation, called the Confederate States of America. They elected Jefferson Davis of Mississippi as their president.

Believing that Lincoln would attempt to force them to rejoin the United States, the Confederacy began to form an army to fight against the federal troops of the North. On April 12, 1861,

Confederate troops bombarded Fort Sumter, a federal fort in Charleston, South Carolina. Lincoln, determined to take back the rebelling states, issued a call to arms in the North. The Civil War had begun. Before long, the armies of the Union and those of the Confederacy were engaged in a terrible conflict that would rage for four bloody years.

For both free blacks and enslaved blacks in America, the first years of the Civil War were a frustrating time. Although the central issue of the war was the enslavement of blacks, blacks themselves were unable to participate in the fight against the Confederacy, and many even found themselves forced to help the southern cause. In the North, blacks were not allowed to join the federal armies. And in the South, slaves were forced to dig trenches and perform other heavy labor for the Confederate troops. Blacks and abolitionists were further disappointed when President Lincoln made no move to emancipate, or free, the slaves of the South.

Frederick Douglass saw the war as a battle not only to preserve the Union but to end slavery in all the states. For Douglass, then, the course of action was clear. "I believed," he later wrote, "that the mission of the war was the liberation of the slave, as well as the salvation of the Union."

As Americans fought Americans on battlefields across the nation, Frederick Douglass was fighting his own war. Touring the northern states, giving dramatic speeches and writing fiery newspaper articles, he demanded that Lincoln emancipate the slaves in the South and allow northern blacks to enlist in the Union armies. But Lincoln felt that freeing the slaves in the South might cause the slave states that had not yet seceded—Delaware, Maryland, Missouri, and Kentucky—to join the Confederacy, making it bigger and stronger. And he was reluctant to allow blacks to enlist in the Union armies. Lincoln felt that the white troops of the North would not accept black soldiers into their ranks. He also felt that the sight of black men in Union uniforms might make the southern troops fight harder.

The Confederate troops, led by General Robert E. Lee, were already fighting hard enough. Although they were outnumbered and outgunned by the Union troops, the rebels were not about to be beaten easily. By late 1862, in fact, the South seemed to be winning the war. Because his armies were having trouble striking an effective military blow against the South, Lincoln decided to strike a moral one.

On September 22, 1862, the president announced the *Emancipation Proclamation*, which stated that, as of January 1, 1863, all slaves in the Confederate states were now free in the eyes of the U.S. government. The proclamation enraged and demoralized white southerners. Blacks everywhere rejoiced. In the South, slaves began streaming off the plantations. For safety, they headed toward areas that were occupied by federal troops. In the North, blacks danced in the streets.

Frederick Douglass heard about the Emancipation Proclamation in a Boston telegraph office. The news, Douglass wrote, was like "a bolt from the sky . . . the dawn of a new day . . . the answer to the agonizing prayers of centuries."

Lincoln's proclamation freed the slaves, but it could not win the war. The Union and Confederate armies fought battle after battle, but the northern troops could not gain an advantage. The battles were gigantic, bloody affairs, and casualties were overwhelming. Lincoln needed more troops if he was to crush the southern rebellion once and for all. He decided that it was time to allow blacks to join the Union forces.

In the spring of 1863, Congress approved the enlistment of blacks into the Union army. Douglass immediately began a recruitment campaign. "Men of Color, to Arms" were his words. It was "Now or Never," he proclaimed. He urged his fellow black men to join the fight against the Confederacy and against the institution of slavery. Soon, black men formed long lines at recruiting stations across the North. The Massachusetts 54th Regiment was the first of many black units in the Union army. Douglass's sons Lewis and Charles were the first black men in New York State to enlist.

The new black soldiers quickly learned that they were not equal to their white comrades (although they were certainly equal when it came to bravery on the battlefield). Racism and discrimination could be found even in the Union armies. Black soldiers were paid only half wages,

A company of black Union soldiers ready to join the fight against the Confederacy in the Civil War. Douglass helped to convince President Lincoln to allow black troops to join the North's armies.

and they received inferior training, meager rations, and inadequate shoes, uniforms, weapons, and other supplies. They were not allowed to become officers, and they were often mistreated by white officers.

When Douglass learned about these conditions, he stopped his recruiting and asked for an appointment with President Lincoln. In the summer of 1863, the two leaders met for the first time. Douglass felt an immediate affection and respect for the great Lincoln. "I at once felt myself in the presence of an honest man," Douglass wrote, "one whom I could love, honor, and trust."

Lincoln listened respectfully to Douglass's concerns. The president promised to bring about whatever changes he could, although he would not be able to solve all the difficulties that black soldiers were facing. Douglass, satisfied that Lincoln was sincere, resumed his recruiting efforts.

Blacks continued to enlist, despite the obstacles that they encountered. Eventually, about 200,000 black troops would serve in the Union armies. As many as 38,000 would be killed or wounded by war's end. The black soldiers distinguished themselves on the battlefield. They were courageous and determined fighters, and they won the grudging respect of even the most prejudiced of their fellow Union soldiers. (Even Confederate soldiers were heard to acknowledge the bravery of the black combatants.) As Lincoln had hoped and as Douglass had known, the black troops began to play an important part in turning the tide of the Civil War.

On the Fourth of July, 1863, Union forces won two crucial victories. At Gettysburg, Pennsylvania, the Army of Northern Virginia, under General Lee, suffered a devastating defeat at the hands of the Army of the Potomac, commanded by General George Gordon Meade. And in Mississippi, the Confederate stronghold of Vicksburg was finally captured by General Ulysses S. Grant after a long, grueling siege.

Despite setbacks in Virginia and Tennessee, by the summer of 1864 the Union armies had the rebels on the run. The forces of the relentless General Grant hammered away at Lee's army throughout the summer and finally trapped Lee and his troops at Petersburg, Virginia. At the same time, Union general William Tecumseh Sherman led a massive army through Georgia and South Carolina on a long, destructive march that left the cities and fields of those states in flames. Clearly, the South could not resist much longer.

In November 1864, Lincoln was elected to a second term of office. Douglass was invited to the *inauguration* ceremony at the White House. Even there, racism cast a long shadow. After attending the president's inaugural speech, Douglass was not allowed into the White House for the reception because he was black. When Lincoln found out, he gave orders for Douglass to be admitted immediately. Inside the White House, the former slave approached Lincoln to congratulate him. "Here comes my friend Douglass," the president said, loudly enough for everyone to hear.

On April 2, 1865, the forces of General Grant captured the Confederate capital of Richmond, Virginia. On April 9, Lee surrendered his sword to Grant at Appomattox Court House, Virginia. The Civil War was over for all but one man. Five days after Lee's surrender, Abraham Lincoln was assassinated at Ford's Theatre in Washington, D.C., by the proslavery fanatic John Wilkes Booth.

On April 14, 1865, the assassin John Wilkes Booth fired a bullet into the head of President Lincoln in the balcony of Ford's Theatre in Washington, D.C.

Freed blacks in the war-ravaged town of Richmond, Virginia, shortly after it was liberated by Union troops in April 1865. Despite their new freedom, blacks in the South still faced poverty and discrimination.

CHAPTER

5

"Our Work Is Not Done"

The nation was shocked and devastated by the murder of Abraham Lincoln. Like most Americans, Frederick Douglass felt a deep sense of loss. At Lincoln's funeral, Douglass gave a speech in which he honored the man who had guided America through the painful and bloody ordeal of the Civil War.

Despite the sadness that he felt, Douglass—and blacks throughout the country—also felt tremendous joy. The battle against slavery had been won. In December 1865, the Thirteenth *Amendment* to the *Constitution of the United States* was approved by Congress. This amendment officially abolished slavery throughout the entire United States. The dream of Frederick Douglass had come true.

Soon, however, the joy felt by American blacks died down as they faced the realities of Reconstruction, the period following the Civil War during which the former Confederate states were readmitted to the Union. Although the North had won the war and slavery had been abolished, blacks began to realize that victorious armies and new laws could not change the racism that still remained in the hearts of many people. Southern plantation owners could no longer keep slaves, but they had no intention of giving blacks equal rights.

Lincoln's vice-president, Andrew Johnson of Tennessee, became president after Lincoln's assassination. Johnson had no sympathy for newly freed slaves living in the hostile environment of the

South, and neither did the men whom he appointed to govern the southern states that were rejoining the Union. Under new laws—called Black Codes—passed by the southern legislatures, blacks in the former Confederate states were oppressed. They could not vote or own land. They were denied all but the most humiliating of jobs. If they remained unemployed, they could be arrested and forced to work under conditions that were not much different from those they had labored under before the Civil War.

Blacks in the Reconstruction South lived in fear. The Ku Klux Klan terrorized them (and white people who were thought to sympathize with blacks). The Ku Klux Klan was (and still is) a secret society believing in the superiority of the white race. Dressed in white, hooded robes, Klansmen went on nightly raids, burning homes, inflicting beatings, and even murdering their victims.

After the war had ended and the Thirteenth Amendment had been adopted, many abolitionists and civil rights activists believed that the fight for freedom and equality for blacks was finished. But Douglass knew that the struggle was not over. "Rebellion has been subdued, slavery abolished, and peace proclaimed," Douglass said, "and yet our work is not done. . . . We are face to face with the same old enemy of liberty and progress. . . . The South today is a field of blood."

In order to combat President Johnson and the other members of the Democratic party who were doing their best to keep the southern states in the hands of racist politicians, Douglass joined forces with Republican politicians who opposed Johnson. Some of these men, known as radical Republicans, wanted to bring sweeping changes to the southern states, such as granting southern blacks the right to vote.

Throughout 1866, Douglass and two radical Republican senators, Thaddeus Stevens and Charles Sumner, campaigned for civil rights for southern blacks. Douglass spoke in towns and cities across the northern states and wrote editorials for magazines and newspapers. Stevens and Sumner used their political skills to carry on the fight in the nation's capital. They scored a victory in the summer of 1866, when Congress passed two bills that President Johnson had attempted to *veto*—the Freedman's Bureau Bill and the Civil Rights Act.

The Freedman's Bureau Bill gave the government more power to provide medical, educational, and financial assistance to former slaves, known as freedmen, in the South. The Civil Rights Act granted full United States citizenship to all black Americans. (In 1867, President Johnson asked Douglass to supervise the Freedman's Bureau programs that were meant to assist former slaves. Douglass turned down the job. He felt that he could not accept such an offer from someone whose beliefs he so fiercely opposed.)

Despite the passing of the Civil Rights Act, several southern states still would not grant blacks

Following the Civil War, Douglass continued his struggle for equality for American blacks. He used his political influence and his powers as a writer and public speaker to pressure the government to pass laws protecting southern blacks from discrimination and to pass laws giving all blacks the right to vote.

the right to vote. President Johnson supported these states, which were resisting other Reconstruction reforms as well. The hostility grew between Johnson and the radical Republicans in Congress. In early 1868, the radical Republicans tried to remove Johnson from office by *impeachment*. They accused the president of trying to take control of the army by illegally dismissing Secretary of War Edwin M. Stanton. This was the first time that Congress had ever attempted to impeach a president. Johnson survived the impeachment trial, but his chances for reelection were badly damaged by the episode.

During the presidential race of 1868, Douglass campaigned for Republican candidate Ulysses S. Grant. Douglass believed that Grant, the former commander of the Union forces during the Civil War, would be a strong supporter of civil rights for blacks. With the help of many black votes, Grant won the election. With the support of the president, Congress then passed the Fifteenth

Amendment, which finally gave black males in all the states the right to vote. Increasing numbers of blacks began to participate in the political process. Blacks from southern states were elected to Congress for the first time. Douglass observed this progress with satisfaction. "I seem to be living in a new world," he said.

In 1872, Douglass's home in Rochester was destroyed by fire. The Douglass family then moved to Washington, D.C. There, Douglass worked as editor for a civil rights newspaper, the *New National Era*. In 1874, Douglass became president of the Freedman's Savings and Trust Company, a bank for black Americans. Unfortunately, the bank failed. Douglass returned to the lecture circuit, where he still drew large crowds.

In 1877, newly elected Republican president Rutherford B. Hayes appointed Douglass U.S. marshal of Washington, D.C. This prestigious, well-paying position enabled Douglass to buy a large house and 15 acres of land near the capital. He named his estate Cedar Hill. Settling down in his spacious new home, Douglass performed his duties as marshal and worked on his third autobiography, *Life and Times of Frederick Douglass*. (His second autobiography, *My Bondage and My Freedom*, had been published in 1855.) Douglass was now 60 years old, and he had come a long way from his days as a slave in Maryland. One day, Douglass traveled from Cedar Hill to Baltimore and paid a visit to his former master Thomas Auld. "Now that slavery was destroyed," Douglass wrote of the encounter, "the slave and the master stood upon equal ground. [Auld] was to me no longer a slaveholder either in fact or in spirit, and I regarded him as I did myself, a victim of circumstances of birth, education, law, and custom."

In 1882, Anna Douglass died. Two years later, Douglass remarried. His new wife was Helen Pitts of Rochester. Friends and relatives of the bride and groom—and American society, black and white—were shocked by the marriage. Not only was Helen Pitts 20 years younger than Douglass, she was white. But Douglass and his new wife were happy together, and they did not let the disapproval of others interfere with their marriage. In 1886, the couple embarked on an extended tour of Europe.

Although Frederick Douglass had achieved success, comfort, and happiness, he could never completely leave behind his life's work. Upon returning to the United States in 1888, Douglass journeyed throughout the Deep South. He was enraged by what he saw. Most blacks in the Deep South still lived under conditions of extreme poverty and oppression. Frederick Douglass began to speak out once again. He demanded equal rights for American blacks and urged blacks to educate themselves and maintain their pride and self-respect.

Aside from a two-year appointment as American consul general to Haiti, Douglass spent

Frederick Douglass died at the age of 77 in 1895. He remained until the end a fierce and eloquent voice of freedom for America's downtrodden peoples.

the final years of his life in the ongoing fight against racism and discrimination. On February 20, 1895, Douglass attended a meeting of women's rights activists in Washington, D.C. There, he was honored for his work on behalf of the feminist movement. That night, at home, he died of a heart attack. He was 77 years old.

During his lifetime, Frederick Douglass was a living symbol of freedom. Against all odds, he rose from slavery to liberty. Once he had achieved his own personal emancipation, he dedicated his existence to the destruction of the institution of slavery in the United States and to the struggle for equal rights for all black Americans (and for women, too). Since his death, his name has become synonymous with the fight for racial justice in America, and he remains an inspiration to all those who are oppressed because of the color of their skin.

Further Reading

Other Biographies of Frederick Douglass

Davidson, Margaret. *Frederick Douglass Fights for Freedom*. New York: Four Winds Press, 1970.

Douglass, Frederick. *The Life and Times of Frederick Douglass*. Adapted by Barbara Ritchie. New York: Crowell, 1966.

McKissack, Pat. *Frederick Douglass, Leader Against Slavery*. Hillside, NJ: Enslow, 1991.

Miller, Douglass T. *Frederick Douglass and the Fight for Freedom*. New York: Facts on File, 1988.

Patterson, Lillie. *Frederick Douglass, Freedom Fighter*. Champaign, IL: Gerrard Tub, 1965.

Chronology

1818   In February, Frederick Bailey, later
known as Frederick Douglass, is born
near Easton, Maryland.

1824   Begins working for his owner, Captain
Aaron Anthony, and he starts his self-
education.

1826   Is sent to Baltimore, Maryland, to work
for Hugh Auld.

1833   Returns to Aaron Anthony's farm and
goes to work for Thomas Auld.

1834   Is sent to work for the notorious "slave
breaker" Edward Covey.

1836   After his first escape plan fails, Douglass is imprisoned briefly and then sent back to Hugh Auld in Baltimore.

1838   Escapes to New York and later sends for and marries Anna Murray; the couple travels to New Bedford, Massachusetts; Frederick Bailey legally changes his name to Frederick Douglass.

1841   William Lloyd Garrison, the leader of the American Anti-Slavery Society, hears Douglass speak at an abolitionist meeting and invites him to go on a lecture tour.

1845   *Narrative of the Life of Frederick Douglass* is published; Douglass travels to Great Britain.

1847   Returns to the United States and moves to Rochester, New York; begins publishing the *North Star.*

1850   Takes charge of the Underground Railroad in Rochester.

1859   Following the John Brown rebellion, travels to Canada and then to Great Britain.

1860	Returns to the United States.
1861	The Civil War begins.
1863	Douglass recruits black soldiers for the Union army and meets with President Abraham Lincoln to discuss their treatment.
1865	The Civil War ends.
1867	Declining President Andrew Johnson's offer to head the Freedman's Bureau, Douglass instead campaigns for civil rights for southern blacks.
1874	Moves to Washington, D.C.; becomes president of the Freedman's Savings and Trust Company.
1877	Is appointed U.S. marshal of Washington, D.C.
1882	Anna Douglass dies.
1884	Douglass marries Helen Pitts.
1889	Is appointed American consul general to Haiti.

1891 Resigns post of consul general; resumes writing and lecturing in the United States.

1895 Frederick Douglass dies in Washington, D.C., on February 20.

Glossary

abolitionist a member of the movement to end slavery

civil rights the personal and property rights recognized by a government and guaranteed by its laws and constitution

Constitution of the United States a document written and adopted in 1787 that established a set of basic principles by which the United States is organized and governed

constitutional amendment an addition or alteration to the United States Constitution

democracy a type of government in which political power is held primarily by the citizens and exercised directly or indirectly through elected representatives

economy the economic processes of a country, state, or region

Emancipation Proclamation   a declaration issued by President Abraham Lincoln in 1862 that freed black slaves in Confederate states

feminist   one who believes that women are entitled to the same political, economic, and social standing as men

free states   states, primarily in the northeastern part of the United States, in which slavery was against the law previous to the Civil War

impeachment   an action by Congress charging the president, vice-president, or another government official with misconduct or abuse of power

inauguration   the formal ceremony in which an official takes office

legislation   the process of making laws through the passage of government acts and bills

racism   a belief that one's own race is superior to other races

secession   the act of withdrawing from membership in a union or organization

segregation   the practice of separating members of a certain group or race from another body or group

slave state   states, primarily in the southeastern part of the United States, in which slavery was permitted previous to the Civil War

Underground Railroad   a network of abolitionists who helped runaway slaves escape to free states or Canada

veto   the power to prevent legislation from becoming law

Index

Picture Credits

The Bettmann Archive: frontis, pp. 16, 20, 22, 26–27, 30, 32, 36, 41, 47, 50, 52, 58–59, 63; Bureau of Agricultural Economics: p. 6; New York Public Library: p. 11

Melissa Banta has been a curator of historic photographs and prints at Harvard University for 10 years. She is the author and editor of a number of publications and exhibitions, including "From Site to Sight: Anthropology, Photography, and the Power of Imagery," and coauthor of "The Invention of Photography and Its Impact on Learning." Ms. Banta also holds a position at the scientific organization Earthwatch, where she is director of photography and a writer for educational video programs. She received a B.A. degree in anthropology from the State University of New York at Buffalo and an M.S. degree in communications from Boston University.